Key Stage 3

Year 7 Workbook

Name: ______________________

Class: ______________________

English

Ian Enters
Sally Hughes

First published 1999

Letts Educational
9–15 Aldine Street
London W12 8AW
Tel 0181 740 2270
Fax 0181 740 2280

Design and page layout: Ken Vail Graphic Design, Cambridge

Illustrations: Sylvie Poggio Artists Agency (Nick Duffy, Rosalind Hudson, Paul McCaffrey, Phil Smith and Sarah Warburton)

British Library Cataloguing-in-Publication Data

A CIP record for this book is available from the British Library

ISBN 1 84085 215 1

Printed and Bound

Letts Educational is the trading name of
BPP (Letts Educational) Ltd

Acknowledgements
Extracts reproduced by kind permission: p16, from *Photographs and Notebooks* by Bruce Chatwin, published by Jonathan Cape; pp22 and 24, from *Messing About in Boats* by Martha Gellhorn, with permission of The Estate of Matha Gellhorn; pp27-30, from *Whale* by David Holman, published by Methuen Publishing Limited and reproduced in support of The Whale and Dolphin Conservation Society; p37, from *The Monster Garden*, © Vivien Alcock 1988, published by Methuen Children's Books, an imprint of Egmont Children's Books Limited, and used with permission

Contents

Introduction: for teachers

This is one of a series of three books, for Years 7, 8 and 9, which have been compiled to support the teaching programme in the Letts *Classbook* for Key Stage 3 English.

Each of the books is free-standing and has been designed so pupils may use it independently, as a 'workbook'. However, it is likely that this book, and the series, will prove most valuable when used in conjunction with the *Classbook* and with each unit of work introduced through classroom discussion.

The intention of the series is to provide a wider range of texts and writing tasks, that give opportunities to reinforce and extend the knowledge and communication skills established through the *Classbook*. Each book does not cover the same genres – or periods – nor attempt to cover the full range of possible genres, but over the series, teachers should find sufficient variety to enable them, in conjunction with the *Classbook*, to address the requirements of the National Curriculum programmes of study for Key Stage 3 English.

Hence, the focus in these books is on understanding and response, and writing practice. The extracts are supported by questions that encourage learning about genre characteristics. A 'twin-pronged' focus on the texts is suggested: detailed consideration of word/sentence issues, and reflection on broader matters of a whole text/genre nature. Each writing task is genre-specific and designed to reinforce the learning acquired in answering the questions, by encouraging pupils to demonstrate their understanding through practice in their own work.

It is also hoped that, over the whole series and within each book, the texts provide a good range in terms of difficulty and interest to pupils. Each teacher will need to guide pupils towards appropriate material, but the intention is that extracts should be stimulating and challenging. Within the series, the Year 7 book is intended to build a bridge between the methods and habits of working of the National Literacy Strategy at Key Stage 2 and secondary school approaches to English. The Year 8 book links with this and leads pupils towards the strategies of the Year 9 book, which is intended to point pupils forward to the work of their GCSE course at Key Stage 4.

Epic story: *Beowulf*

This extract from *Beowulf*, re-told by Kevin Crossley-Holland and illustrated by Charles Keeping, is taken from a modern re-telling of a poem which dates from the eighth century. The poem tells of the heroic deeds of the warrior Beowulf. In his youth, Beowulf fights and kills the monster Grendel which has been attacking Heorot, the great hall of Hrothgar, the Danish king. In this extract the reader learns that Heorot is still not safe for the Danes. Grendel's mother has appeared.

As you read, think about:

- the way that speech is used to create excitement and drama
- the impression the reader has of Beowulf from what he says, does and how others relate to him
- the difficulty of the journey he undertakes with his men.

In the middle of the night, two servants with flaming torches roused Beowulf from his sleep and escorted him to Hrothgar's chamber. 'Aeschere!' said the king. He shook his head and his face creased, a grey grief-map. 'Now Aeschere!'

'I am here,' Beowulf said.

'Aeschere is dead. My dear old friend, my battle companion'.

'In the hall?'

'Two monsters! Just as some men have said, there are two monsters after all, rulers of the moors, rangers of the fell-country. Grendel and his mother, and it will never end.'

'It will end,' Beowulf said.

'She came to Heorot,' said the king. 'She barged into the hall, mournful and ravenous, snatched down Grendel's grasp from the gable, seized the nearest man – Aeschere! My friend!'

'Vengeance,' Beowulf said.

'She just tucked him under her arm, and made off into the darkness.'

'There is honour amongst monsters as there is honour amongst men. Grendel's mother came to the hall to avenge the death of her son.'

'Once again, Beowulf, help may be had from you alone.'

'Do not grieve,' Beowulf said.

'Her lair is away and over the misty moors, at the bottom of a lake.'

'Better each man should avenge his dead, as Grendel's mother has done. Your days are numbered and my days are numbered...'

Beowulf put a hand on the old king's arm. 'He who can should win renown, fame before death. That is a warrior's best memorial in this world. I promise you, Hrothgar, that wherever she turns – honeycomb caves, mountain woods – I will hunt her down.'

As soon as night eased, Beowulf's stallion, one of Hrothgar's gifts, was saddled and bridled. He left Heorot at once, accompanied by the king, his own companions and a large group of Danes.

They followed the monster's tracks through the forest and over the hills. Then they headed into little-known country, wolf-slopes, windswept headlands, perilous ways across boggy moors. They waded through a fissure, picked their way along string-thin paths, skirted small lakes where water-demons lived; at last they came to a dismal wood, stiff with hoar-frost, standing on the edge of a precipice.

Working on the text

Verbs that show speech

1 Notice how the writer only uses 'said' or uses no verb after direct speech.

- Find the sections where no saying verbs are used.
- Explain why the writer does this. (Think about **what** is being said and **how** it is said.)

2 Now replace 'said' with more interesting verbs, to show tone of voice or feeling. (Look back at the extract before choosing the replacements.)

- *'Aeschere!'* ____________ *the king.*
- *'It will end,' Beowulf* ____________ .
- *'Vengeance,' Beowulf* ____________ .
- *'Do not grieve,' Beowulf* __________ .

Verbs that describe action

1 Highlight the **verbs** used to describe Grendel's mother's actions. Explain how the choice of verbs helps the reader understand the monster's **actions, feelings** and **strength**.

2 Highlight the **verbs** in the last paragraph. List them.

Explain what they show about the journey made by Beowulf and his men and the land they travel through.

Metaphors

1 *'…his face creased, a grey grief map'*

The king's face shows his great sadness at the death of his friend. The lines on his face are described as being like contour lines on a map. His face has lost any colour through the shock.

2 *'honeycomb caves'*

Explain or draw this image.

3 Grendel's mother is said to have a *'lair'*. What is shown about the creature by using the word 'lair' and not 'home'?

4 Highlight and list the nouns used about the **places** on the journey. Then list the adjectives that describe each place.

Adjective	Noun

Writing practice

In your work on the text you have seen:

- how speech adds to the drama and pace of the story
- how verbs suggest more than action
- the effect of carefully chosen images and adjectives.

The extract ends on a **cliff-hanger**. All soap operas use this technique at the end of episodes so viewers will watch to see **what happens next**.

Beowulf and his men have literally arrived at the edge of a cliff, and the next section of the story will deal with Beowulf's battle with Grendel's mother.

Write about Beowulf's next adventure.

Make your writing lively and interesting. Use the techniques you have learnt in this unit.

- You could plan your story using this frame.

Structure and ideas	Notes on details and useful vocabulary
Seeing Grendel's mother for the first time	
Beowulf's words to his men and their reactions	
The battle – weapons? – the struggle – equally matched? – gory?	
The end of the conflict	

Classbook reference
Units 3, 7, 12, 16, 17, 19.

2 Official guide: Mount Rainier

This extract is the opening section of an official guide to Mount Rainier, a mountain in Washington state, in north-west America. The guide aims to give information and to persuade the reader to visit the mountain.

In this unit you will be marking the text as a way of gathering important information. This technique can help you go back to important sections quickly when you are answering questions. This is what many people do when they are making notes or revising.

You will be using different types of reading as you work through the unit:

- **skimming** – reading quickly to get a general understanding of the text
- **scanning** – looking for key sections or words
- **close reading** – reading every word carefully to get a full understanding of the details.

As you read, think about:

- the way the passage is written to gain the reader's attention – its tone and style
- how the mountain is made interesting to the reader – the persuasive power of the writing
- how much information is given – geographical knowledge.

Mount Rainier

Welcome to a mountain wonderland of dense forests, dazzling wild flowers, tremendous snowfields, and rugged glaciers. Enjoy the fresh smell of trees and soil, the soothing – and sometimes deafening – sound of falling water, and the refreshing cold breezes off the glaciers. Towering above all this scenic display is magnificent Mount Rainier.

This is a complex landscape, but the explanation of its origins are simplicity itself: fire and ice. The mountain is a volcano born of fire and built up above the surrounding country by repeated eruptions and successive flows of lava. It is a relatively young volcano, only about one million years old. By contrast, the mountains of the Cascade Range that Mount Rainier looks down upon are at least 23 million years old, created by the folding, buckling and uplifting of the Earth's surface.

Mount Rainier is not an isolated volcano, for from Lassen Peak in California to Mount Garibaldi in British Columbia an entire line of volcanoes defines the north-south march of the Cascades. These peaks dominate the skyline, ever a reminder that they are only dormant and may at any time, like Lassen Peak in 1914-21 and Mount St Helen's in 1980, erupt in fury and rage at the fragile world built by humans. One of the unexpected side benefits of these eruptions has been the deposition of ash and pumice layers that are rich in nutrients and support the abundance of wild flowers throughout the mountainous Pacific North-West.

Even as volcanic forces were building up this land, the slow, inevitable power of glacial ice began to shape and form it. Glaciers come from the snow that does not melt from year to year – it accumulates to greater and greater depths. The weight of the snow presses the air out, packs it tight, and compresses it into ice. Gravity pulls the ice down the mountainside, both scouring and smoothing the bedrock as it goes. Freezing and thawing break rocks from the adjacent stones, and they fall onto the glacier's surface. More debris is picked up by the passing ice. This is an inexorable process that continues today and will alter the mountain in the tomorrows to come. Yes, the process is simple, but it deals in forces that are beyond the control, and perhaps comprehension, of humans. Take a look at this mountain; it may be gone in a million years.

Welcome to a mountain wonderland of dense forests, dazzling wild flowers, tremendous snowfields, and rugged glaciers. Enjoy the fresh smell of trees and soil, the soothing – and sometimes deafening – sound of falling water, and the refreshing cold breezes off the glaciers. Towering above all this scenic display is magnificent Mount Rainier.

This is a complex landscape, but the explanation of its origins are simplicity itself: fire and ice. The mountain is a volcano born of fire and built up above the surrounding country by repeated eruptions and successive flows of lava. It is a relatively young volcano, only about one million years old. By contrast, the mountains of the Cascade Range that Mount Rainier looks down upon are at least 23 million years old, created by the folding, buckling and uplifting of the Earth's surface.

Mount Rainier is not an isolated volcano, for from Lassen Peak in California to Mount Garibaldi in British Columbia an entire line of volcanoes defines the north-south march of the Cascades. These peaks dominate the skyline, ever a reminder that they are only dormant and may at any time, like Lassen Peak in 1914-21 and Mount St. Helen's in 1980, erupt in fury and rage at the fragile world built by humans. One of the unexpected side benefits of these eruptions has been the deposition of ash and pumice layers that are rich in nutrients and support the abundance of wild flowers throughout the mountainous Pacific North-West.

Even as volcanic forces were building up this land, the slow, inevitable power of glacial ice began to shape and form it. Glaciers come from the snow that does not melt from year to year – it accumulates to greater and greater depths. The weight of the snow presses the air out, packs it tight, and compresses it into ice. Gravity pulls the ice down the mountainside, both scouring and smoothing the bedrock as it goes. Freezing and thawing break rocks from the adjacent stones, and they fall onto the glacier's surface. More debris is picked up by the passing ice. This is an inexorable process that continues today and will alter the mountain in the tomorrows to come. Yes, the process is simple, but it deals in forces that are beyond the control, and perhaps comprehension, of humans. Take a look at this mountain; it may be gone in a million years.

Working on the text

Word and sentence work

1 Highlight the adjectives and nouns from paragraph 1 (including proper nouns). List them.

2 The mountain is **personified**, that is, it is described in language usually used about people. List these words and phrases from paragraph 2, e.g. *'a volcano **born** of fire'*.

3 Highlight and list words and phrases used in paragraph 3 to show the difference between the power of the volcanoes and the people who live nearby.

4 List all the words from the whole extract that are normally used in **geography** and **geology**.

5 Underline or highlight the words in the extract whose meaning you do not know.

- How much, if at all, did this stop you understanding the passage? Not at all/a little/quite a lot/a lot.
- Put a circle around the words whose meaning you were able to work out without looking in a dictionary.
- Explain **how** you worked out **one** of these words.

Text and genre work

Use your notes from the word and sentence work to help with the text questions.

1 Write a factual account of what a visitor to Mount Rainier would see (avoid description).

This is an area ______________________________

____

2 Explain how **personification** helps the reader imagine the volcano and how it developed.

3 Explain in your own words the advantages and disadvantages of living near this volcano.

4 Paragraph 4 describes the process of glaciers eroding the mountain. Number the stages in the correct order.

☐ The ice moves down the mountainside, drawn by gravity, and wearing down the rocky surface.

☐ Deep snow builds up over years at high altitudes.

☐ The moving ice collects more and more rock and broken stone, and continues to wear down the mountain's surface.

☐ The snow packs down, turning into ice.

☐ Rocks accumulate on the glacier, broken from the surface rocks by changing temperatures.

Writing practice

Use the notes you made when you were working on the text to answer these questions as **fully** as you can. Whenever possible use short quotations to support your answers.

1 Write about paragraph 1 of the text. Comment on the following points:

- the impression of Mount Rainier a reader would get from a factual account
- the impression the reader gets from the official guide
- explain which account is more convincing for a person thinking about making a visit.

2 Explain how the reader gets the impression of the size and power of Mount Rainier and the other volcanoes.

3 Explain why a friendly tone is used at the beginning and end of the text, i.e.:
'Welcome to a mountain wonderland...'
'Take a look at this mountain...'
Comment on:

- who would be reading the piece (the audience)
- why they would be reading it (the purpose)
- the intended effect.

4 This extract uses vocabulary normally used in the study of geography and geology. Explain how the text avoids sounding like a textbook. Comment on:

- the purpose and the audience
- the use of description
- the use of personification.

5 Write a factual account that aims to give **information** about a coastal area. You can use the following features as a starting point:

- beach
- cliffs
- steep paths
- rock pools
- dunes
- sea.

6 Write a **description** of the same area. This time aim to persuade the reader to visit this place. Use the following techniques:

- a friendly tone
- use of adjectives
- use of personification.

7 Write a short paragraph to explain how you made the second description a **persuasive** piece of writing. Use short quotations from your work to show this.

Classbook reference
Units 2, 4, 19.

Ballad: *The Wife of Usher's Well*

This is a ballad: a song story with regular rhyme and rhythm. We do not know who created it. We do not know who Usher might have been, where or what his 'well' was, or how 'the wife' came to be linked with the 'well'. The anonymous teller and writer must have assumed that the audience knew all these things and much more besides. We do know that it dates from the seventeenth century. You will need to read between the lines and think about the pronunciation of some of the words. The modern translation of some words is given.

As you read, think about:

- alliteration
- repeated words, phrases and clauses
- the atmosphere created by these effects
- spot who says and does what, when and why
- decide which characters are alive and which are dead and how they feel about each other.

It will help to read the poem aloud all the way through before concentrating on details.

The Wife of Usher's Well

There lived a wife at Usher's Well
  And a wealthy wife was she;
She had three stout and stalwart sons
  And she sent them o'er the sea.

They hadna been a week from her,
  A week but barely ane,
Whan word came to the carline wife
  That her three sons were gane.

They hadna been a week from her,
  A week but barely three,
When word came to the carline wife
  That her sons she'd never see.

'I wish the wind may never cease,
  Nor fishes in the flood,
Till my three sons come hame to me
  In earthly flesh and blood.'

It fell about the Martinmas
  Whan nights are lang and mirk,
The carline wife's three sons came hame
  And their hats were o' the birk.

It neither grew in syke nor ditch
  Nor yet in ony sheugh,
But at the gates o' Paradise
  That birk grew fair eneugh.

'Blow up the fire, my maidens,
  Bring water from the well;
For a' my house shall feast this night
  Since my three sons are well.'

And she has made to them a bed,
  She's made it large and wide,
And she's ta'en her mantle her about,
  Sat down at the bed-side.

Up then crew the red, red cock
  And up and crew the gray;
The eldest to the youngest said,
  ''Tis time we were away.'

The cock he hadna crawed but once
  And clapped his wings at a'
Whan the youngest to the eldest said,
  'Brother, we must awa'.

'The cock doth craw, the day doth daw,
  The channerin' worm doth chide;
Gin we be mist out o' our place
  A sair pain we maun bide.

'Fare ye weel, my mother dear;
  Fareweel to barn and byre;
And fare ye weel, the boony lass
  That kindles my mother's fire'.

carline old   *birk* birch   *syke* small stream   *sheugh* trench   *channerin'* fretting

Working on the text

Text and genre work

1 Complete the following information:

Characters: ______________________________

Wife's age: ______________ Wife's wealth: ______________

Wife's attitude towards sons: ______________________

Why do you think we don't learn the characters' names? ______________

Who might Usher be? ______________

2 What might the wife have wanted her three sons to do or be when she sent them over the sea? (fishermen, migrants to another country, merchants, other reasons)

3 What do you think might have happened to the husband and sons? (shot, drowned, died from natural causes, murdered by wife, swallowed by a whale, other ideas)

- Explain how you reached your opinions.

4 What does the wife pray for in verse 4 and how does her prayer come true?

She prays that ______________ until her sons ______________ .

5 Where have the three sons come from in '*earthly flesh and blood*' (verses 4, 5 and 6)? (the dark night, Martinmas – the day on which St Martin's life is celebrated in the Christian calendar – heaven, from the top of a birch tree)

- Use a quotation to support your answer.

6 How are the three creatures that appear to warn the sons described through their colour and what they do?

Noun	Adjective	Verb
cockerel	red	crows

7 The sons say goodbye to their mother and another character in the last verse.

- Who is the final character to appear, and why do you think she is important to the sons?

Word and sentence work

1 Highlight the **alliteration** on the consonant 's' in the last two lines of verse 1.

- What might the adjectives '*stout*' and '*stalwart*' mean?

2 What is the **dialect form** of the words '*had not*' in verses 2 and 3?

3 Which **vowel** would be the **standard English form** in the words '*ane*' and '*gane*' in verse 2?

4 Where have the three sons left their hats in verses 5 and 6? Which letter has been omitted from the phrase '*o' the birk*'? What is the missing letter in the words '*channerin'* ' and '*daw*' in verse 11?

- Explain why you think these letters have been omitted.

5 There is to be a party '*since my three sons are well*'.

- Where are the three sons placed in verse 8, which suggests that they are not the life and soul of the party?

6 There are lots of **numbers** one, two, and three in the poem. Count the numbers:

a) Number of sons? Which sons speak? How many of them? Which is missed out?
b) Weeks in verse 2?
c) Weeks in verse 3? Which is missed out?
d) Number of cockerels? How many times do the cockerels crow?
e) Number of '*farewells*'?

7 There are lots of phrases and clauses with **pairs** of things compared or contrasted (in antithesis).

e.g. '*stout*' and '*stalwart*', verse 1; '*syke nor ditch*', verse 6; '*The cock doth craw, the day doth daw*', verse 11.

- Find three other examples and give their meaning in standard English.

Writing practice

Practise the ballad form. To create your own ballad you need:

- a simple story line
- a four-line, 8/6/8/6 syllable count for each verse
- rhymes on the second and fourth lines
- alliteration – repeated phrases and patterns.

Use the following framework to generate a three-verse ballad and then try to develop your own.

Here are some words to fit into the gaps, but you may find better ones yourself. (*he, shrimpy, how, lived, dwelt, pearls, crabby, farmed, wrinkled, castle*)

There ____________ an ancient, ____________ man (8 syllables)
And a ____________ was he (6 syllables)
He made a ____________ in the sand (8 syllables)
And __________ the ___________ sea. (6 syllables. 'Sea' rhymes with 'he' in second line.)

A mermaid, hoping to be wed, (8 syllables)
Discovered where ____________ (6 syllables)
She gave him ____________ she gave him ____________ (8 syllables)
She showed him ____________ she felt. (6 syllables. 'Felt' to rhyme with the last word of second line)

But little did the ancient man (8 syllables)
Take notice of her charms. (6 syllables)
Her tail was seaweed green and long (8 syllables)
And limpets were her arms. (6 syllables)

Create your own ballad

- You could use the following writing frame for your own ballad's first verse:

There lived ___________________ (8 syllables)
Who was ___________________ (6 syllables)
She ___________________ (8 syllables)
And ___________________. (6 syllables, last word rhyming with last word of second line)

Classbook reference
Units 14, 20.

4 Travel writing: Bruce Chatwin

Bruce Chatwin kept notes, diaries and photographs of his travels. After his death at an early age, these were published. During his short life he wrote a number of travel books and described the way of life of forgotten and dying tribes. The passage comes from his notes when he was travelling in Mauritania, Africa.

As you read, think about:

What 'ingredients' do travellers' notebooks contain?

- short, vivid descriptions of what catches the eye and mind
- missed-out words and phrases in sentences: ellipsis
- feelings and reactions to events and scenes
- observations without obvious connections
- the voice of the author in the first person singular and their personal style of writing.

What does the title of the extract mean? What language is it?

En Marche

The happiness that is to be found sleeping under tents is unbelievable. One night in tents is worth three in town. Wonderful effect of the horizon framed in the curve of the tent. Impression of heaven, of the roundness of the vault of the sky – flat land spreading out from the tent.

The fort of the French, the flagpole. The cool pink arched officers' rooms. A Foreign Legion hat and a pile of Hennessy bottles. The latrines were engulfed in sand.

The country purple and grey, tufts of bleached grass sometimes pale green sometimes gold. All along the road there are skeletons of animals – camels, donkeys and goats, their skeletons stuck in the last spasm of desiccating thirst, bones bleached with fragments of skin adhering.

We came to a place where brilliant acid yellow plants played over steel blue rocks.

I have been talking to young Peul. No one has ever looked and dressed in a more utterly magnificent manner – with his almond green trousers, yellow jacket and orange and white scarf. The flatness of face, the incredible sensitivity of the lips – the smile – the linear angularity of the mouth, the body sculptured, lithe and vigorous.

'Peanuts', they say here, 'cause cancer'.

Working on the text

List examples of each of the following ingredients in the passage. You are given one example of each element to help you. Try to explain how each quotation works.

1 Short, vivid descriptions

• Colours and pictures in words	*'brilliant acid yellow plants'*: adjectival phrase of three adjectives together to describe plants *Your examples and comments:*
• Objects	*'fragments of skin adhering'*: reminds me that these bones were once alive, covered with flesh and blood *Your examples and comments:*
• People and creatures	*'linear angularity of the mouth'*: geometrical term – lips in lines at an angle to each other – means he's smiling – why not just say that? *Your examples and comments:*
• Scenes	*'roundness of the vault of the sky'*: the tent is round and so is the sky – both are in harmony *Your examples and comments:*

2 Feelings and reactions to events and scenes

• Consider how the writer shows humour, happiness, a sense of awe and wonder, awareness of beauty, sadness and ugliness.	'*sleeping under tents*': in contrast to sleeping in towns gives a feeling of happiness. *Your examples and comments:*
• Mixed feelings Not all the reactions are positive or negative. Some are mixed. Consider whether Bruce Chatwin shows more than one feeling in any of his observations.	'*Peanuts,' they say here, 'cause cancer.*' It sounds like a joke, but is a serious idea. It emphasises that people seem to jump to conclusions. The fact that '*they say here*' occurs in the middle of the line makes the ending more like a punch line. *Your examples and comments:*

3 Observations without obvious connections

• Between sections/paragraphs	Tent moves to French fort – no joining *Your examples:*
• Between sentences	'*sometimes gold. All along the road there are skeletons…*' *Your examples:*

4 Missed-out words/phrases: ellipsis

• Find all the dashes in the passage and consider what may have been missed out and what you are expected to guess.	*'vault of the sky – flat land spreading out from the tent.'*: there is no main verb. I think I am expected to put in something like 'leads the eyes down to the…' *Your examples and comments:*
• Short sentences or clauses linked by a comma without main verbs. Look particularly at the second section of the notebook for examples.	*'officers' rooms. A Foreign Legion hat…'*: I think these objects were seen inside the rooms. A full sentence might read: 'Inside the cool pink arched officers' rooms was a Foreign Legion hat and a pile of Hennessy bottles'. *Your examples:*

5 Voice of the author

• First person	'*We came to a place...*' This shows that Bruce Chatwin was not alone on his travels, although he normally talks about 'I'. In this passage he only uses the first-person form twice, but lots of the words missed out would have been 'I saw' or 'I noticed'.
• Colloquial phrases and personal style	'*Wonderful effect*' is an example of Bruce Chatwin's enthusiasm. *Your examples and comments:*

• Particular interests Bruce Chatwin seems to notice some things more than others. From reading this passage, what do you think are his main interests in life?	I think Bruce Chatwin is interested in the unusual things of life and may exaggerate what he experiences. He describes Peul as '*utterly magnificent*' because of what he wears and how he looks. *Your examples:*

Writing practice

Imagine you are in a place for the very first time – perhaps a place you visited on holiday recently. Imagine you are writing a notebook description for somebody who has never been there. Follow Bruce Chatwin's style of writing to show atmosphere, details and feelings.

Classbook reference
Unit 4

Travel writing: Martha Gellhorn

Fiction invents stories and tries to make them real in our minds. Non-fiction describes reality, which sometimes sounds stranger than fiction. The text in this unit is non-fiction.

Travel writing is a genre often found in magazines and newspapers. It has a long history. Historians from the earliest days have accompanied armies along routes to conflict. Their writing describes the places visited and the events that occurred. Contemporary travel writing continues the tradition and, occasionally, it is war correspondents who create the most vivid pictures from the war front.

Martha Gellhorn, who died in 1997 in her mid-eighties, was a travel writer and journalist of distinction. She wrote fiction (11 novels) and non-fiction (war and travel documentaries). She was also a television and radio broadcaster.

This extract comes from her *Travels with Myself and Another*. 'Messing About in Boats' was written in 1942, about the Caribbean.

As you read, think about:

- Martha Gellhorn's view of Jean and his wife
- Jean's view of his wife
- how the reader's ideas are influenced by the narrator (the 'I' of the passage)
- what other views of the situations and characters could be considered?

Working on the text

Every time he tried to go, he was struck down. On his first attempt to escape, he had lost his boat, a complete shipwreck, and was lucky to get back in the dinghy. Since then, when a rare passer-by offered transport, he was always stopped by paralysing illness. He unfolded this weird tale in bright sunshine, while we smoked and swung our legs from the jetty. Assuming he was not a nut, he had been on this spooky island too long. I told him bossily that voodoo spells were rot and he could come with us and make his way to England from Antigua. Bossiness seemed to invigorate him. He would join the good ship *Pilot* but asked that we sail at night and swore me to secrecy lest the witch hear of his plans.

He then took me home, a woven reed hut in the jungle, and I too was impressed by the witch. She was beautiful; tall, lavishly curved, smooth brown skin, thick wavy brown hair to her shoulders and long green eyes. Standing in the doorway, with her hands on her hips, she stared at the peeling blonde visitor with undisguised contempt and dislike. I couldn't think how to respond. Cringe or snub? Jean, apparently sure of himself by daylight, ordered her to bring food. Rice and lobster and fried bananas. Delicious. Perhaps her cooking compensated for her witchcraft. She moved slowly, graceful as a panther, showing resentment in every gesture. She refused to speak or eat with us.

Commentary and questions

Paragraph 1

'He was struck down every time he tried to escape. He had lost his boat on his first...'

- Compare this version with the original. The author uses a different word order. What is the effect of reversing the main and subordinate clauses/phrases?
- What impression do these words create? How does it encourage you to read more?
  - *'unfolded this weird tale in bright sunshine'*
  - *'rare passer-by'*
  - *'assuming he was not a nut'*
  - *'spooky island...voodoo'*
  - *'spells'*

Paragraph 2

- Pick out the adjectives and the simile (comparison using 'as' or 'like') used to describe the 'witch'.

  Compare these adjectives with the way the writer describes herself.
- Notice that some ideas come in pairs in this paragraph:
  - *'contempt and dislike'*
  - *'Cringe or snub'*
  - *'refused to speak or eat'*
- What good thing does the 'witch' do? What are the 'witch's' feelings towards the visitor? Why might she behave as she does?

Answers

Carlton was furious over the night departure. 'Ain't no reason for it. I doan know dese waters. Stoopid. I gotta tink for de *Pilot*.' I insisted, having promised Jean, and having seen the witch. I'd be jolly glad myself to get away from those baleful green eyes. Around midnight, Jean showed up on the jetty, his teeth chattering in his head, his eyes bloodshot. He was running a high fever; it was all he could do to walk to the harbour to tell me not to wait. Rescue was impossible, he would never be able to leave; he saw his fate with despair. Clearly he believed in black magic, but I figured his demon lover could doctor his food with inedible mushrooms, snake venom, cat piss, whatever she found handy and bad for the digestion, every time he acted restless. I urged him to come anyway, sick as he was; perhaps the witch's spell wore out by nautical miles. He wouldn't risk my safety, the weather was uncertain enough without evil incantations.

I thought about him as a tragic figure; I imagined his life chained to the green-eyed sullen witch until she tired of him, whereupon she would brew a poisonous spell and do him in. Ten years later, I met Jean again on St Martin. He had a pretty wife and baby, a real house above a dazzling beach, and a pleasure boat. I dared not ask questions and he offered no information about the witch or his release from her clutches. He looked healthy, happy and prosperous.

Commentary and questions

Paragraph 3

- Change the dialect speech into standard form and structure. *'Ain't no reason...*de *Pilot'.*
- What makes the writer insist on leaving at night? Change the sentence (*'I insisted...witch'*), keeping its meaning, using 'because' rather than the participle 'having'.
- What makes the 'witch' appear increasingly threatening as the passage continues? Consider the use of words like *'baleful'*, *'demon lover'*, *'black magic'*, *'evil incantations'*, as well as how the writer imagines the doctoring of Jean's food.
- *'Perhaps the witch's spell wore out by nautical miles'*.

  What is the narrator suggesting?

Paragraph 4

- What sort of life does the writer imagine Jean has?
- She is wrong. Could she have been wrong about the supposed 'witch'?
- What parts of this passage read like fiction? Which elements convince you it is real travel writing?

Answers

Writing practice

Jean's wife is described as a beautiful 'witch' intent on trapping her husband in a jungle hut for the rest of his life. The narrator believes this description, but Jean manages to escape. We do not know how he managed to leave, but Jean's 'witch' wife could tell us the truth.

Use the table below to develop the story as told by Jean's 'witch' wife. Consider using the following ideas:

- Jean drinks heavily
- Jean is criticised by his white friends for marrying a black woman
- the white woman makes Jean's wife feel inferior because she is poor
- Jean's wife is the daughter of a local black doctor. She knows how to use herbs.

You could use this writing frame or use your own structure and ideas.

Order of events and ideas	**Your story from the wife's point of view (you can use these sentence starters if you want)**
The background to Martha Gellhorn's visit The wife's feelings	I was ashamed of our hut in the jungle when Jean brought white people to visit, and I was angry at feeling so ashamed for was not my father as good as his father and my home as good as any other's? I knew he told them stories about me, saying that I kept him with me through witchcraft. All lies, but who would believe me?
The visit and the food	One day, during the hottest season before the great storm…
The wife's feelings towards Martha Gellhorn's bossiness	Jean had often complained, saying he would leave me, but how could I let my husband go with such a woman? She…
The argument with Jean that evening	He had drunk too much as usual and kept saying he would leave me and go on the *Pilot*. I wanted to throw him out, but shame prevented me. Was I not his wife to love and cherish him? I…
Jean returns from the ship, with a fever and trembling. He suffers from malaria.	He is a weak man, this Jean of mine. But I will nurse him through his madness. When the new year comes, however, there must be other ways of living. I…

Classbook reference
Units 4, 9, 14, 19.

Drama: *Whale*

This play, *Whale* by David Holman, was written about real events that took place in Alaska in October 1980. Three Californian grey whales were trapped by the thickening ice of the Arctic Ocean and were unable to reach their usual route to warmer waters.

The play begins with the Storyteller, two Inuit characters and the Raven. In the stories of this part of the world, Raven is a powerful, clever, often mischievous, character.

Notice that people from this area are called Inuit, which means 'the people'. Consider why this is preferred to the name Eskimo, which means 'eaters of raw fish'.

As you read, think about:

- how David Holman gives us a sense of time and place
- how the text is set out
- how the scene would look in the theatre.

Act One

Scene One

With strong Inuit drum accompaniment the Storyteller comes forward. Drumming breaks up the introduction.

STORYTELLER Tavvauvussi sursit. (Greetings to you, young ones.) Greetings, young ones, from the people of the northern ice. Home of the seal, home of the white bear, home of the whale.
From the very ancient times we have lived together with the whale. We cannot live without the whale, the whale cannot live without us. We are the people of the whale.
But we know that, one morning, we may go down to the edge of the ice and no longer hear the call of the whale because the great ships have killed them all. That is why we bring our story. So that the whale which is in our hearts will live also in yours.
It is a story that begins before there were whales in the sea, before there were seals, before arctic fish swam, before the first white bear prowled the ice flows.

Lights come up on the igloo.

STORYTELLER When all the world was empty except for an old man and an old woman.

The two Inuit appear. An Old Man and an Old Woman. They are lightly singing a song in Inuktitut.

Sunavinuk?
Arvingunavuguk?
Vugungnai?
ai ai ai ai
Arvingudlunu
Pinasuartaulaarpugungai?
(What shall we be?
Shall we be whales?
Shall we?
ai ai ai ai
Being whales
We will be hunted, won't we?
ai... ai... ai... ai.)

The Storyteller narrates over the whale song.

STORYTELLER They lived all alone on a small island of ice in the middle of the icy sea.

The Old Woman takes a vessel from the igloo and comes slowly forward to the edge of the stage.

STORYTELLER One day the old woman came down to the sea to get water.

The Old Woman lies down on the ice while the Old Man goes on singing and working.

Storyteller	Not seeing that across the sea was floating towards her – a feather. A black, black feather. And the feather floated right into her mouth.
Old Woman	Aghhhhhhhhhhhhhhhh.
	The Old Man stops singing and looks at her as she runs back to him, holding her stomach.
Old Woman	Ajjigingititausimavunga! (Look what's happened to me!)
	As the Old Woman tells the Old Man what has happened to her the Storyteller continues.
Storyteller	Time passed and the old woman's stomach grew bigger and bigger and one day she gave birth – to a raven.
	The baby Raven is born, and flies to top of igloo.
Raven	Caaaaaaaaaaaaaawwwwwwwwww.
	The Raven is a lively, mischievous but slightly funny figure. He caws continuously. The parents try to get it down and baby it. There is a moment of calm and they cuddle the Raven.
Both Inuit	Ohhhhhhhhhhhhhhhhhhhhhhh.
Storyteller	The man and woman loved their baby but it was the most mischievous child that ever came into the world.
Raven	Cawwwwwwwwwwwwwwwwwwwww.
Storyteller	Sometimes they were in despair.
Raven	Cawwwwwwwwwwwwwwwwwwwww.
Storyteller	One day they had something to do and they shut their baby up for a few moments in their house of ice.
	They shut the Raven into the house.
Raven	Cawwwwwwwwwwwwwwwwwwwww.
Old Man	Tigusingilaurit nuka piak. (Don't touch anything.)
Storyteller	And please don't you dare touch anything, youngster. And especially don't touch the bladder. Back soon. Rub noses.
	The Raven calms and makes to cry.
Both Inuit	Ohhhhhhhhhhhh.
	They leave, supporting each other, so tired with the baby Raven.
Raven	Cawwwwwwwwwwwwwwwwwwwww.
Storyteller	Since the beginning of time a large bladder had hung from the ceiling. The couple didn't know what was in it, but they knew it should never be touched.
Raven	Cawwwwwwwwwwwwwwwwwwwww.
	And the igloo turns round to show the Raven and the bladder. He is pecking at everything on ground level. Then he looks up and sees the bladder. Looks interested.
Raven	Cawwwwwwwwwwwwwwwwwwwww.
	He starts to look as though he might peck at it.

STORYTELLER Until that moment all the world had been dark. Though nobody knew it, it was because all the light in the world was locked up for safety in the bladder. No, Raven!!!!!!
The Raven pecks at the bladder. Bright lights and harsh sounds flood the stage. Raven looks very confused.

RAVEN Cawwwwwwwwwwwwwwwwwwwwww.
Both Inuit rush on.

BOTH INUIT Aghhhhhhhhhhhhhhhh.

RAVEN Cawwwwwwwwwwwwwwwwwwwwwww.!!!!!!!!!!

STORYTELLER Suddenly the whole world was flooded with light. The old man and the old woman rushed to stop all the precious light escaping.
They do so. The Raven is still screaming and looking sorry for himself. The Old Woman closes the bladder while the Old Man beats the Raven on the bottom. He howls.

OLD MAN Irnikulualuga! (Look what you've done, my child!)

STORYTELLER Half the light had escaped before the old woman could close the bladder. And that is why, from that moment, the world has had both day – and night.
Back to the original lighting.

OLD MAN Tulugagulualuk! (You naughty raven!)

OLD WOMAN Aksualuk aniqujaudlutigit ikumak. (You've let out so much light.)
They shake their heads and leave. The Raven starts to cry again. Then calms.

Working on the text

Text and genre work

1 Look carefully at the way this piece of script is set out on the page.

- Think about the ways in which this is different from the way you set out a story.
- List rules you could give for writing a play. (Think about page layout, showing speech, punctuation used and action.)

Use the heading **'Rules for writing a playscript'**

Number your ideas, e.g.:

1 Plays are set out in acts and scenes.

2 ________________________________

Aim to work out at least six ideas.

2 This play takes place in Alaska. How is the audience given a sense of where the action happens? Use quotations.

3 How does David Holman begin to show Raven's character? Think about:

- words
- voice
- actions
- relationships
- costume
- what is said about Raven.

4 The character of Raven is played by an actor. List four problems you foresee for the actor playing this part, and their solutions. (Look carefully at the stage directions as well as the dialogue.) Example: Raven needs to fly, so the actor will need to move like a gymnast.

5 **a)** Explain – or draw – your ideas for staging this scene.

b) Explain the sound and lighting effects you could use in this scene.

6 This scene uses the ancient story of how day and night came to the world. In your own words, summarise the Inuit story of Raven stealing the light. Write one or two paragraphs, including all the main details (100–150 words).

Word and sentence work

1 The storyteller uses words and phrases that quickly convey that this is a story that has been told many times, e.g. '*It is a story that begins before there were whales in the sea...*'. Find some more examples.

Suggest what the writer would want the audience to feel as they listen and watch.

2 Think about traditional stories you know. List some of the phrases that are regularly used, e.g. 'once upon a time...'. Aim to collect at least five.

3 When Raven releases the light everything happens very suddenly. List the words and phrases that capture the sense of speed and panic. Add words of your own.

4 Find and list examples from the scene where words and phrases are repeated, e.g. '*Home of the seal, home of the white bear, home of the whale*'. Explain why the writer uses repetition. What effect does this achieve?

5 Look at the following nouns and create adjectives. Use your adjectives with appropriate nouns. Notice that you will be using several different suffixes and different spelling rules here.

Noun	Adjective and noun	Spelling rule
ice	*e.g. icy sea*	*Drop the –e to add –y*

Now do the same with: fun, home, mystery, drama, revenge, magnet, adventure.

Writing practice

Use the summary below of the opening of *Raven and the First Men* to create a playscript. Consider: • how plays are set out • staging, lighting and sound • Raven's words, voice, actions and relationships • the humour of the story.

> Raven was bored. He strutted up and down the sandy beach looking for something to amuse himself. Nothing. He cried out with a loud, exasperated yell.
>
> Suddenly, he heard a small, muffled squeak. He searched until he found the source of the sound – a giant clamshell that was full of tiny creatures. The creatures were very afraid of Raven and so he coaxed and used all his tricks to encourage the creatures out of the shell to play.
>
> Eventually some of the shell-dwellers found the courage to emerge from their home. They looked very strange to Raven – no beaks, wings or feathers, instead they had pale skin and stick-like arms. These were the first humans.

Classbook reference

Units 4, 11, 16.

Prose fiction: Monstrous creations

Mary Shelley wrote *Frankenstein* in 1818. Since then it has remained popular with readers and filmmakers. In the novel, Victor Frankenstein is a talented scientist with a dream. He wants to create life, and in his attempt he uses parts of dead bodies to make his creature. This extract is where he brings his creation to life.

As with many other novels and short stories, *Frankenstein* is written in the first person, 'I', the **first-person narrative**.

This has **advantages** for the author:

- she can describe Frankenstein's feelings in detail
- the reader feels closer to the narrator because they understand the narrator's thoughts and feelings
- she can recount events and show the intensity of the times.

Of course, there are **disadvantages** too:

- she can only tell what the narrator witnesses; everything else is secondhand
- the reader gets a biased view of events through the narrator's eyes.

As you read, think about:

- how you can tell that this was written almost 200 years ago
- the use of the first-person narrative
- the way the writer uses contrasting ideas
- the description of the monster
- the way that Victor Frankenstein reacts to his creation.

It was on a dreary night of November that I beheld the accomplishment of my toils. With an anxiety that almost amounted to agony, I collected the instruments of life around me, that I might infuse a spark of being into the lifeless thing that lay at my feet. It was already one in the morning; the rain pattered dismally against the panes, and my candle was nearly burnt out, when, by the glimmer of the half-extinguished light, I saw the dull yellow eye of the creature open; it breathed hard, and a convulsive motion agitated its limbs.

How can I describe my emotions at this catastrophe, or how delineate the wretch whom with such infinite pains and care I had endeavoured to form? His limbs were in proportion, and I had selected his features as beautiful. Beautiful! Great God! His yellow skin scarcely covered the work of muscles and arteries beneath; his hair was of a lustrous black, and flowing; his teeth of pearly whiteness; but these luxuriances only formed a more horrid contrast with his watery eyes, that seemed almost of the same colour as the dun-white sockets in which they were set, his shrivelled complexion and straight black lips.

The different accidents of life are not so changeable as the feelings of human nature. I had worked hard for nearly two years, for the sole purpose of infusing life into an inanimate body. For this I had deprived myself of rest and health. I had desired it with an ardour that far exceeded moderation; but now that I had finished, the beauty of the dream vanished, and breathless horror and disgust filled my heart. Unable to endure the aspect of the being I had created, I rushed out of the room and continued a long time traversing my bedchamber, unable to compose my mind to sleep.

Working on the text

1

Highlight, in different colours, all the words that:

- create a picture of **darkness** and **lack of life**
- create a picture of **light** and **potential for life**.

Darkness and lack of life	Light and potential for life
• dreary	• instruments of life
•	•
•	•
•	•
•	•
•	•
•	•
•	•

♦ Notice how the **contrast** is made between the surrounding darkness and gloom and the anticipation of new life created by the scientist, Frankenstein.

2

Highlight, in different colours, all the words that:

- create a picture of **ugliness or disaster**
- create a picture of **attractive features**
- mark the words 'horrid contrast' in another colour.

Mary Shelley now develops her writing to show 'the horrid contrast' in the creature Frankenstein has created.

Disaster/ugly features	Attractive features
•	•
•	•
•	•
•	•
•	•
•	•
•	•

♦ Notice how the **balance** of these two ideas makes the monster seem more repulsive than if it had been described only in negative terms.

3

- Highlight the key words which show Frankenstein's feelings.

Remember, a **prefix** is a letter or group of letters added to the beginning of a word to make a new word.

e.g. **semi-** precious: semi-precious
circle: semi-circle

Prefix and meaning	**in–** in or into	**in–** to make an opposite	**un–** to make an opposite
From the text	**in**fuse	**in**animate	**un**able
Add words that use this prefix in the same way			

4 Some readers find this older language difficult. Try to match these words from the passages with their corresponding expressions. You may need to use a dictionary.

beheld	bedroom
convulsive motion	saw
wretch	crossing
endeavoured	passion
lustrous	tried very hard
ardour	shining
traversing	become calm after being upset
bedchamber	a wicked or unfortunate person
compose	with violent and uncontrolled movements

5 Describe Frankenstein's reactions when his creation comes to life. Comment on:

- how long he had worked on the project
- how the monster looked
- what Frankenstein did
- Mary Shelley's choice of words.

The next extracts are from *The Monster Garden* by Vivien Alcock, which was written in 1988. The main character, Frankie Stein, is the daughter of a scientist and, like Victor Frankenstein, she sets out to create a new life. At this point of the novel her 'creation' is about to be given life through the power of the storm.

You will be using the structure of this piece as a starting point for your own writing.

As you read, think about:

- the use of the first person, 'I', especially showing the character's thoughts
- how the ordinary and the extraordinary are shown
- the use of short sentences
- the use of contrast (as in *Frankenstein*).

It thundered in the night. I woke up and lay watching the lightning cracking the sky. How vivid it was. It made me blink. I am not in the least frightened of thunderstorms, coming as I do from a scientific family. But I had never seen lightning like this before. It came leaping towards my window as if it wanted to come in. So quick, so bright! It hurt my eyes.

So I shut them, and turning to face the wall, went back to sleep. I didn't remember that my window was still open at the bottom. I did not think of my monster at all. I didn't dream.

In the morning, I woke to the sound of water flushing through the cistern. (My room is next to the bathroom.) I heard the door open and shut and footsteps going down the passage. David. Then I remembered.

I sprang out of bed and ran over to the window. The saucer on the sill had cracked and was oddly blackened, as if it had been rubbed with soot. There was nothing in it. David was right. I was too young to be trusted to look after things.

Oh well, never mind, I thought.

It must have been very windy in the night. The window sill was still wet and one or two seed pods had blown on to it. The carpet felt damp under my feet. Then I noticed that all the petals had gone from the African violets, and the few leaves that remained were tattered as if –

I stepped back. As if something had bitten pieces out of them!

Then I saw it.

It was in the far corner of the window sill. Squatting there. Not moving. It had grown during the night. Now it was the size of those pale toadstools you find at the roots of trees in Burners Wood. Silvery grey in colour, humped in the middle and thinning towards a transparent, crinkled edge. While I slept, the dark spot in the centre must have grown and split. It now had two red eyes and they were looking at me.

Nonsense, I told myself. But I did not move.

It twitched.

Slowly, horribly, it began to squirm and slither over the sill towards one of the seed pods. Then it stopped. A growth came out of its side, like a short fat tentacle, and pounced. The tentacle drew back into the body. I saw the seed pod twist and wriggle as the grey, half-transparent flesh simmered around it like thick stew. Then it was gone.

I bit my lip hard. Interesting, I told myself. Fascinating. Instructive.

I hated it. I wished it were dead.

After studying the passages, carefully read the notes alongside each text extract. Re-read each paragraph and make sure you understand the points being made.

1

Notice the balance of short and longer sentences. She uses the short sentences to emphasise ideas, e.g. thunder, brightness of lightning, no dreams.

It thundered in the night. I woke up and lay watching the lightning cracking the sky. **How vivid it was. It made me blink**. I am not in the least frightened of thunderstorms, coming as I do from a scientific family. But I had never seen lightning like this before. It came leaping towards my window as if it wanted to come in. **So quick, so bright! It hurt my eyes**.

So I shut them, and turning to face the wall, went back to sleep. I didn't remember that my window was still open at the bottom. I did not think of my monster at all. **I didn't dream**.

2

Short sentences mark a change of pace in the paragraph. Her brother reminds her about her experiment.

In the morning, I woke to the sound of water flushing through the cistern. (My room is next to the bathroom.) I heard the door open and shut and footsteps going down the passage. **David**. **Then I remembered.**

3

Notice the character's thoughts made clear.

I sprang out of bed and ran over to the window. The saucer on the sill had cracked and was oddly blackened, as if it had been rubbed with soot. There was nothing in it. David was right. I was too young to be trusted to look after things.

Oh well, never mind, I thought.

It must have been very windy in the night. The window sill was still wet and one or two seed pods had blown on to it. The carpet felt damp under my feet. Then I noticed that all the petals had gone from the African violets, and the few leaves that remained were tattered as if –

Setting the scene for the discovery of the monster:
- unusual events
- lightning provides the spark of life for the creature.

Make notes here for your writing

Set the scene: use a combination of short sentences and more detailed sentences – time, place, atmosphere

Turning point: it seems like an ordinary day until she remembers.

Make notes here for your writing

Turning point: seems ordinary until…

Tension/suspense: strange events but also a delay. This forms a **false start.**

Make notes here for your writing

Tension/suspense: perhaps a false start

4

I stepped back. **As if something had bitten pieces out of them!**

Then I saw it.

5

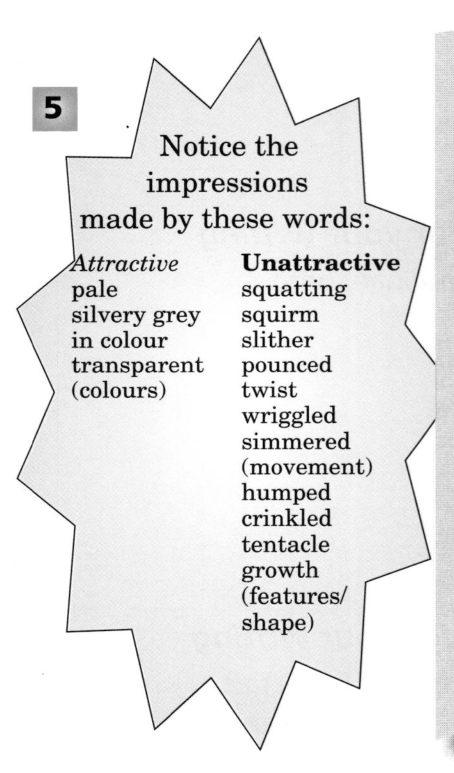

It was in the far corner of the window sill. **Squatting** there. Not moving. It had grown during the night. Now it was the size of those *pale* toadstools you find at the roots of trees in Burners Wood. *Silvery grey in colour*, **humped** in the middle and thinning towards a *transparent*, **crinkled** edge. While I slept, the dark spot in the centre must have grown and split. It now had two red eyes and they were looking at me.

Nonsense, I told myself. But I did not move.

It twitched.

Slowly, horribly, it began to **squirm** and **slither** over the sill towards one of the seed pods. Then it stopped. A **growth** came out of its side, like a **short fat tentacle**, and **pounced**. The tentacle drew back into the body. I saw the seed pod **twist** and **wriggle** as the **grey, half-transparent flesh simmered** around it like **thick stew**. Then it was gone.

6

Notice
the character's
thoughts made
clear.

I bit my lip hard. Interesting, I told myself. Fascinating. Instructive.

I hated it. I wished it were dead.

Revelation: the short sentence ('*Then I saw it*'.) suggests that details will follow.

Make notes here for your writing

Revelation: your monster is about to be revealed

Description: of the monster

Notice the **contrast** as in Mary Shelley's *Frankenstein*

Make notes here for your writing

Description: use contrast

Narrator's reactions: Frankie's reactions are similar to Victor Frankenstein's

Make notes here for your writing

Reactions: physical actions as well as feelings

Writing practice

Write a short story in which someone creates a new form of life:

- write in the first person
- follow the structure suggested in the preceding section
- use the knowledge you have gained from *Frankenstein* and *The Monster Garden* to help you write descriptively and vividly
- ensure you make the creator's feelings clear (these need not be the same as in the two extracts)

Classbook reference

Units 1, 16, 20.

Poetry: Gerda Mayer

8

Gerda Mayer was born in Karlsbad, Czechoslovakia, in 1927, and came to England in 1939, just before the German army invaded her native country. She has lived in England since then. *Babes in the Wood* was started in 1962 and *Hansel and Gretel* in the late 1970s, but both deal with serious matters of childhood insecurity. Gerda Mayer called them her Hansel and Gretel poems.

The traditional tale of *Babes in the Wood* tells of two young children deserted in the forest and left to die, but rescued from an evil witch through their own intelligence and the kindness of the forest creatures.

You will come to understand the following terms as you explore the poems. They will become clear as you work through the questions.

- allegory
- alliteration and assonance
- personification
- regular and irregular rhythm
- satire.

Babes in the Wood

for L.M. Hans and Susi Kraus

There is a well known story
Of two little children who crossed
A dark and dangerous forest
And in that forest were lost.

The crumbs they had strewn for their safety
Were picked up by a bird;
The trees had ears and gathered
Every whispered word.

They came to a hut in a clearing,
The name on the door said HATE;
Hate hacked them into pieces
And cooked them in the grate.

*'O forester, hear our voices!
World, pity our cry!'*
The forester came to dinner;
The world went rolling by.

The world said *'It's unlikely
That such things can occur;'*
(Besides she feared their rescue
Would leave the brats with her).

Alas for the Happy Ending
Of how the tables were turned;
There was no reversal of fortune –
It was Hansel and Gretel who burned.

Working on the text

Word and sentence work

1 The first verse is one complete sentence with no punctuation at the end of the first three lines. It sounds like the opening to a fairy story, but there are **poetic devices** at work.

- Complete the tables below.

Find the **end rhymes** (repeated sound at the ends of words)

End rhymes		

Find the **assonance** (repeated sounds within words)

Assonance	story			forest	

Find the **alliteration** (repeated sounds at the beginning of words)

Alliteration		dangerous

2 The first line of the second verse is longer than others, with a carry-over into the second line. There is another carry-over from line 3 to line 4.

- Consider the following reasons for the way the verse is written and add your thoughts.

	Meaning of lines	**Explanation**
Lines 1 and 2	A bird **picked** up the crumbs. The children had made a trail of crumbs so that they could find their way out of the forest. The bird **betrayed** them.	The first line is long to show how long the trail of crumbs must have been. I wonder why the poet puts '*picked up*' instead of '*eaten*'. It makes the bird's action seem more sinister, as if it knows that it will trap the children. Keeping the words '*a bird*' until the end of the two lines keeps you guessing who took the crumbs. *Your thoughts:*
Lines 3 and 4	The trees **listened** to the children's conversation **like spies** instead of friends.	Wheat and corn have '*ears*', but trees do not. *I think…*

3 Gerda Mayer originally wrote the following verse 3:

Original

They came to a hut in a clearing
the name on the door said WRATH
Wrath cut them into pieces
And put them into a broth.

Final version

They came to a hut in a clearing,
The name on the door said HATE;
Hate hacked them into pieces
And cooked them in the grate.

- Identify the changes and say why you think they were made.

'the name' – 'The name'	This looks as if the capital T was missed out in the first version. I think the poet put in punctuation later. There's a comma at the end of the first line now…
'WRATH' – 'HATE'	
'cut' –	
'put them into a broth' –	

- Which version do you prefer and why?

4 There are examples of **personification** in the poem (a thing or idea described in language normally used about people).

- Complete the table below.

The trees had ears	The trees are turned into people acting as informers and collaborators listening to whispers and betraying the children.
HATE	
world	

5 What is the effect of changing '*children*' into '*brats*' in verse 5?

6 Capital letters are used for the words '*the Happy Ending*'. Why?

Text and genre work

1

- A story that carries a hidden meaning is called an **allegory**.
- A story that carries a hidden meaning and a moral about how people should behave is called a **parable**.
- A story that carries a hidden meaning and criticises the powerful through ridicule is called **satire**.
- This poem is a **satirical allegory**.
- It is written in the form of a **ballad**.
- It satirises the terrible acts of Nazi Germany by using the language of a nursery tale.

You will need to know what happened during the Second World War.

- Find out about the following words:

Word	Explanation
Nazi	
Gestapo	
concentration camps	
gas ovens	
Jews	
informers	

2 Fill in the table below to show the hidden meaning (**allegory**):

What the story says	Allegory
Two children were lost in a forest. Despite their attempts to find their way out, they failed.	People in Czechoslovakia tried to escape when the Germans invaded their country. Many had kept their money and personal possessions, but these were stolen by…
They came to a hut, but the owner killed and burned them.	They were placed in concentration camps where they thought they might be safe, but…
Their deaths were not discovered. People could not believe there was such evil at work.	
There was no miracle rescue. Once dead, the children stayed dead.	

The Hansel and Gretel House

When you come across it
you'll know better than to nibble.
'*Who's there?*' asks the witch.
'*The wind,*' cry the
startled children.

A house may look sweet
from outside: beware!
Things happen in pretty houses
you wouldn't believe…

When the wind cries,
when the dog weeps,
when the voice of lost children
is heard in the wood,
let the forester hasten forth.

Word and sentence work

1 The opening lines of the poem use the pronoun 'you'.

- To whom is the poet writing, do you think? (children, adults, witches, everybody and anybody reading the poem)
- Explain your reasons. You might choose more than one of these audiences.

2 The opening line of the poem uses the pronoun 'it'.

- How do you know that 'it' refers to the Hansel and Gretel house?
- Give two reasons.

3 Look at the speech in italics.

- Who are the speakers?
- Explain why the children are '*startled*'.

4

- What adjectives are used in verse 2 to describe how a house may look?
- Why should children beware of attractive exteriors?
- What is the reason for the ellipsis (…) at the end of the verse?
- How would the meaning and feeling be changed if the last two lines read:
  'You wouldn't believe that
  Things happen in pretty houses.'

5 Practise reading the last verse to emphasise its meaning and feeling to a listener who cannot see the text.

- Fill in the table below, adding any other thoughts you have.

Line from the poem	**Number of syllables – suggested tone, intonation, pace, volume**	**Stress on words or parts of words – meaning and feeling**
'*When the wind cries*'	4 syllables – strong and slow	Stress '*when*'/'*wind*'/'*cries*'; personification of *wind*
'*when the dog weeps*'	same syllables as first line –	
'*when the voice of lost children*'	7 syllables; first 3 like previous 2 lines	
'*is heard in the wood*'	5 syllables – different rhythm to first 2 lines. '*is heard*' refers back to the '*voice of lost children*'	Stress '*heard*' and…
'*let the forester hasten forth*'	8 syllables; assonance and alliteration in '*forester hasten forth*' makes the line hurry along '*forth*' means…	The forester represents an adult who cares for…

Text and genre work

1 Pick out the similarities and differences between the two poems and fill in the table below, adding your own ideas and thoughts.

Similarities	Differences
Same traditional tale: *Babes in the Wood* and *Hansel and Gretel*	First poem in regular ballad rhythm; second poem irregular rhythm
The hut and house both threaten and hurt the children.	The house is attractive and deceptive; the hut is clearly full of hatred.

Writing practice

- What are the two poems about?
- What did Gerda Mayer hope to achieve by writing and publishing these poems?
- How successful has she been?

Use the following plan to build up a piece of writing which shows your thoughts about the two poems and answers the questions as well as you can. Imagine the reader is someone who does not know the poems. An introduction is provided, but you may wish to change and add to it. Guidance is given for each of the sections so you can write in an essay form.

Introduction: explain what you are going to do in your essay; explain the background to the two poems and your first thoughts about them.	e.g. This essay is about two poems by Gerda Mayer. I am going to describe how the poems are put together and the meanings they carry. By doing this I shall work out some of the reasons why the poems may have been written. The poems are *Babes in the Wood* and *The Hansel and Gretel House*. When I first saw the titles, I thought that the poems would just tell the nursery story, but I quickly found there were hidden meanings to explore…
Development: describe each poem in turn, picking out the main features and your ideas about each. This should take between four to six paragraphs; two/three for each poem. Don't be afraid to include short quotations. Use the terms **allegory** and **personification** and the information about the Second World War, if you can.	*Babes in the Wood* seems very simple and innocent at the beginning, reminding me of 'once upon a time' type stories: '*well known story*', '*two little children*' and '*dark and dangerous forest*' are just the sort of phrases heard in nursery tales. The second verse continues to sound… By the third verse, however, it is clear that vicious evil is at work. The hut…
Main issues: explain the importance of the hidden meanings and the effect of the style of the poems on you. You need to pick out the main similarities and differences. Use your earlier work to help you. This should take about two paragraphs.	The main issues in these poems are to do with how things that appear sweet and innocent can actually be ugly and evil. *The Hansel and Gretel House* describes… I think it is saying… *Babes in the Wood*, however,…
Conclusion: bring together your main points and give your own thoughts about why the poems were written and how effective they are at getting their message across. This section should be one or two paragraphs long.	In both poems, Gerda Mayer is describing how people can be destroyed by cruelty. The first poem relates to… The second poem deals with… I think Gerda Mayer wrote the poems to show… My own conclusions about the poems are that…

Classbook reference

Units 15, 19, 20.

9 A traditional tale

People have always told stories, often using them to explain what has seemed miraculous and inexplicable. The best stories are told and told again, passing down through generation after generation. *Raven Steals the Light*, a traditional tale of the Haida from the north-west coast of America, re-told by Bill Reid, is one version of such a story. You met the same story in Unit 6 as a playscript.

As you read, think about:

- the sequence or order of events in the story
- the character of Raven
- grandparents' feelings for their grandchildren
- the style of the story and how it shows that it has been told aloud many times.

1 BEFORE THERE WAS ANYTHING, before the great flood had covered the earth and receded, before the animals walked the earth or the trees covered the land or the birds flew between the trees, even before the fish and the whales and seals swam in the sea, an old man lived in a house on the bank of a river with his only child, a daughter. Whether she was as beautiful as hemlock fronds against the spring sky at sunrise or as ugly as a sea slug doesn't really matter very much to this story, which takes place mainly in the dark.

2 Because at that time the whole world was dark. Inky, pitchy, all-consuming dark, blacker than a thousand stormy winter midnights, blacker than anything anywhere has been since.

3 The reason for all this blackness has to do with the old man in the house by the river, who had a box which contained a box which contained an infinite number of boxes each

nestled in a box slightly larger than itself until finally there was a box so small all it could contain was all the light in the universe.

4 The Raven, who of course existed at that time, because he had always existed and always would, was somewhat less than satisfied with this state of affairs, since it led to an awful lot of blundering around and bumping into things. It slowed him down a good deal in his pursuit of food and other fleshly pleasures, and in his constant effort to interfere and to change things.

5 Eventually, his bumbling around in the dark took him close to the home of the old man. He first heard a little singsong voice muttering away. When he followed the voice, he soon came to the wall of the house, and there, placing his ear against the planking, he could just make out the words, 'I have a box and inside the box is another box and inside it are many more boxes, and in the smallest box of all is all the light in the world, and it is all mine and I'll never give any of it to anyone, not even to my daughter, because, who knows, she may be as homely as a sea slug, and neither she nor I would like to know that.'

6 It took only an instant for the Raven to decide to steal the light for himself, but it took a lot longer for him to invent a way to do so.

7 First he had to find a door into the house. But no matter how many times he circled it or how carefully he felt the planking, it remained a smooth, unbroken barrier. Sometimes he heard either the old man or his daughter leave the house to get water or for some other reason, but they always departed from the side of the house opposite to him, and when he ran around to the other side the wall seemed as unbroken as ever.

8 Finally, the Raven retired a little way upstream and thought and thought about how he could enter the house. As he did so, he began to think more and more of the young girl who lived there, and thinking of her began to stir more than just the Raven's imagination.

9 'It's probable that she's as homely as a sea slug,' he said to himself, 'but on the other hand, she may be as beautiful as the

fronds of hemlock would be against a bright spring sunrise, if only there were light enough to make one.' And in that idle speculation, he found the solution to his problem.

10 He waited until the young woman, whose footsteps he could distinguish by now from those of her father, came to the river to gather water. Then he changed himself into a single hemlock needle, dropped himself into the river and floated down just in time to be caught in the basket which the girl was dipping in the river.

11 Even in his much diminished form, the Raven was able to make at least a very small magic – enough to make the girl so thirsty she took a deep drink from the basket, and in doing so, swallowed the needle.

12 The Raven slithered down deep into her warm insides and found a soft, comfortable spot, where he transformed himself once more, this time into a very small human being, and went to sleep for a long while. And as he slept he grew.

13 The young girl didn't have any idea what was happening to her, and of course she didn't tell her father, who noticed nothing unusual because it was so dark – until suddenly he became very aware indeed of a new presence in the house, as the Raven at last emerged triumphantly in the shape of a human boychild.

14 He was – or would have been, if anyone could have seen him – a strange-looking boy, with a long, beaklike nose and a few feathers here and there. In addition, he had the shining eyes of the Raven, which would have given his face a bright, inquisitive appearance – if anyone could have seen these features then.

15 And he was noisy. He had a cry that contained all the noises of a spoiled child and an angry raven – yet he could sometimes speak as softly as the wind in the hemlock boughs, with an echo of that beautiful other sound, like an organic bell, which is also part of every raven's speech.

16 At times like this his grandfather grew to love this strange new member of his household and spent many hours playing with him, making him toys and inventing games for him.

17 As he gained more and more of the affection and confidence of

the old man, the Raven felt more intently around the house, trying to find where the light was hidden. After much exploration, he was convinced it was kept in the big box which stood in the corner of the house. One day he cautiously lifted the lid, but of course could see nothing, and all he could feel was another box. His grandfather, however, heard his precious treasure chest being disturbed, and he dealt very harshly with the would-be thief, threatening dire punishment if the Ravenchild ever touched the box again.

18 This triggered a tidal wave of noisy protests, followed by tender importuning, in which the Raven never mentioned the light, but only pleaded for the largest box. That box, said the Ravenchild, was the one thing he needed to make him completely happy.

19 As most if not all grandfathers have done since the beginning, the old man finally yielded and gave his grandchild the outermost box. This contented the boy for a short time – but as most if not all grandchildren have done since the beginning, the Raven soon demanded the next box.

20 It took many days and much cajoling, carefully balanced with well-planned tantrums, but one by one the boxes were removed. When only a few were left, a strange radiance, never before seen, began to infuse the darkness of the house, disclosing vague shapes and their shadows, still too dim to have definite form. The Ravenchild then begged in his most pitiful voice to be allowed to hold the light for just a moment.

21 His request was instantly refused, but of course in time his grandfather yielded. The old man lifted the light, in the form of a beautiful, incandescent ball, from the final box and tossed it to his grandson.

22 He had only a glimpse of the child on whom he had lavished such love and

affection, for even as the light was travelling toward him, the child changed from his human form to a huge, shining black shadow, wings spread and beak open, waiting. The Raven snapped up the light in his jaws, thrust his great wings downward and shot through the smokehole of the house into the huge darkness of the world.

23 That world was at once transformed. Mountains and valleys were starkly silhouetted, the river sparkled with broken reflections, and everywhere life began to stir. And from far away, another great winged shape launched itself into the air, as light struck the eyes of the Eagle for the first time and showed him his target.

24 The Raven flew on, rejoicing in his wonderful new possession, admiring the effect it had on the world below, revelling in the experience of being able to see where he was going, instead of flying blind and hoping for the best. He was having such a good time that he never saw the Eagle until the Eagle was almost upon him. In a panic he swerved to escape the savage outstretched claws, and in doing so he dropped a good half of the light he was carrying. It fell to the rocky ground below and there broke into pieces – one large piece and too many small ones to count. They bounced back into the sky and remain there even today as the moon and the stars that glorify the night.

25 The Eagle pursued the Raven beyond the rim of the world, and there, exhausted by the long chase, the Raven finally let go of his last piece of light. Out beyond the rim of the world, it floated gently on the clouds and started up over the mountains lying to the east.

26 Its first rays caught the smokehole of the house by the river, where the old man sat weeping bitterly over the loss of his precious light and the treachery of his grandchild. But as the light reached in, he looked up and for the first time saw his daughter, who had been quietly sitting during all this time, completely bewildered by the rush of events.

27 The old man saw that she was as beautiful as the fronds of hemlock against a spring sky at sunrise, and he began to feel a little better.

Working on the text

Text and genre work

1 Explain why Raven wanted the world to have light.

2 Describe how Raven managed to find a way into the home of the old man and his daughter.

3 Describe how the young child was like the Raven (refer to paragraphs 14 and 15).

4 Explain how and why the old man finally allows the Ravenchild to hold the light. (Use the information in the passage, but also explain what you imagine the old man was thinking and feeling at this point in the story.)

5 Many stories – especially myths – use **personification**. In this story Raven has many human qualities.

- Complete the table below.
- Use evidence from the story and add to the list of human characteristics shown by Raven.

Raven's human characteristics

Characteristic	**Evidence from the story (use quotations or your own words)**
impatient, dissatisfied	from paragraph 4:
curious	from paragraph 5:
	from paragraph 6:
determined	
clever and cunning	
	from paragraph 20:

Word and sentence work

1 Look carefully at these two **similes** from the story (a simile compares one thing with another to create a new and fresh picture).

- The old man's daughter is described as possibly being either:

'beautiful as hemlock fronds against the spring sky at sunrise'

or

'**ug**ly as a **s**ea **slug**'

- The **similes**, as well as creating a picture, also use the sounds of the words to create their impressions. The soft and soothing sounds of the **alliteration** 's' adds to the attractive picture of delicate leaves against the bright promise of sunrise, while the **assonance** of the short 'u' sound coupled with the hard 'g' is definitely as unattractive to most people as the picture of a slug!
- Now create two similes beginning 'as beautiful as…' and two beginning 'as ugly as…' (Think carefully about the pictures your similes create and the sound they make.)

2 Look at this sentence structure carefully. You are going to use the same pattern in your own writing.

'…the whole world was dark. Inky, pitchy, all-consuming dark, blacker than a thousand stormy winter midnights, blacker than anything anywhere has been since.'

This gives us a sense of there being absolutely no light at all.

- In the next three sentences convey the sense of bright light, loud noise and intense cold.
- Fill in the blanks. Think carefully about your choice of words.

a) The whole world was light. ______________, ______________, ______________ light, brighter than a ______________ ______________ ______________ ______________, brighter than anything anywhere has been since.

b) The whole world was noise. ______________, ______________, ______________ noise, louder than ______________ ______________ ______________ ______________, louder than anything anywhere has been since.

c) The whole world was cold. ______________, ______________, ______________ cold, more intense than ______________ ______________ ______________ ______________, more intense than anything anywhere has been since.

3 Some words are built up from the **root** by adding **prefixes** and **suffixes**. In the word 'radiance', the **root** is 'radi' (from the Latin, meaning 'light, a ray or a spoke') and the **suffix** is 'ance' (meaning 'the quality of').

- Read the box below from left to right and see how many words you can find with 'radi' as the root.
- List them.

ir		cal		
	radi	o		
		ance		
		ant		**e.g. radiant, radius**
		at	e	
			or	
			ion	
		us		

- Take the word 'fuse' from the Latin *fundere* (which means to melt, pour). Read the box below from left to right, adding as many prefixes and suffixes as possible.
- List the words you create.

	fus	e	
de		ing	**e.g. defuse**

Writing practice

'*How Raven Freed the Moon*' is yet another version of the same story, but this time it has been written for children by Anne Cameron.

RAVEN is the trickster.

She never uses force.

She uses her wits and her magic, and sometimes outsmarts herself.

Raven is often good, sometimes bad; Raven is always beautiful.

Above all else, Raven loves beautiful things, especially bright, shiny things.

One day, Raven heard the people talking about an old fisherwoman and her daughter who lived on an island far to the north and had a round, bright, shiny thing they called Moon which they kept in a beautiful carved cedar box, locked away from those who might want to steal it.

Raven wanted the Moon.

Raven flew all day in the bright sunlight. Heading north, she flew over the rivers and streams, over the mountains and valleys, over the trees and beach, searching for the old fisherwoman and her daughter, searching for the round, bright, shiny Moon.

Raven flew all night through the darkness. In the sky there were only pinpoints of light as the stars tried to light her way.

Finally, just when Raven thought she was too tired to go any further, she arrived at the house of the fisherwoman and her daughter.

Quickly, Raven used her magic. She turned herself into a lovely little baby girl, lay down by the door and began to cry.

Inside the cedar log house the fisherwoman stirred restlessly. Then she sat up, rubbed her eyes and looked around her house. Everything was exactly as it should be.

So she lay back down again.

Raven, who was no longer a bird, but a lovely little baby girl, took a deeper breath and cried even more loudly.

'What's that?' the fisherwoman demanded.

'It sounds like a baby,' replied her daughter.

'There's no baby around here,' the fisherwoman said firmly.

'Still,' the daughter puzzled, 'it does sound like a baby.'

Raven could hear their voices. She took several deep breaths and howled at the top of her voice.

'My heavens!' the fisherwoman gasped. 'It certainly does sound like a baby.'

This is your chance to be the writer. You will need to consider how Anne Cameron has started the story:

- line length
- use of direct speech
- descriptive writing.

Continue the story *How Raven Freed the Moon* in the same style as Anne Cameron.

Classbook reference
Units 1, 5, 16, 19.